Books by Raymond Briggs:

Jim and the Beanstalk
The Elephant and the Bad Baby
The Mother Goose Treasury
The Fairy Tale Treasury
Father Christmas
Father Christmas Goes on Holiday
The Complete Father Christmas
Fungus the Bogeyman
The Snowman
The Snowman Pop-Up
The Snowman Address Book
The Snowman Birthday Book
Gentleman Jim
When the Wind Blows
The Fungus the Bogeyman Plop-Up Book
The Tin Pot Foreign General and the Old Iron Woman

RAYMOND BRIGGS

The Complete Father Christmas

Comprising 'Father Christmas' & 'Father Christmas goes on Holiday'

HAMISH HAMILTON
London

HAMISH HAMILTON CHILDREN'S BOOKS

Published by the Penguin Group
27 Wrights Lane, London W8 5TZ, England
Viking Penguin Inc, 40 West 23rd Street, New York, New York 10010, U.S.A.
Penguin Books Australia Ltd, Ringwood, Victoria, Australia
Penguin Books Canada Ltd, 2801 John Street, Markham, Ontario, Canada L3R 1B4
Penguin Books (N.Z.) Ltd, 182-190 Wairau Road, Auckland 10, New Zealand

Penguin Books Ltd, Registered Offices: Harmondsworth, Middlesex, England

First published in Great Britain 1978 by
Hamish Hamilton Children's Books

Copyright © 1978 by Raymond Briggs

5 7 9 10 8 6
ISBN 0 241 10036 4

FATHER CHRISTMAS
© 1973 Raymond Briggs
All rights reserved
First published in Great Britain 1973 by
Hamish Hamilton Children's Books
15 17 19 20 18 16 14

FATHER CHRISTMAS GOES ON HOLIDAY
© 1975 Raymond Briggs
All rights reserved
First published in Great Britain 1975 by
Hamish Hamilton Children's Books
10

Printed and bound in Italy by Arnoldo Mondadori Editore

Father Christmas

For my Mother and Father

Father Christmas

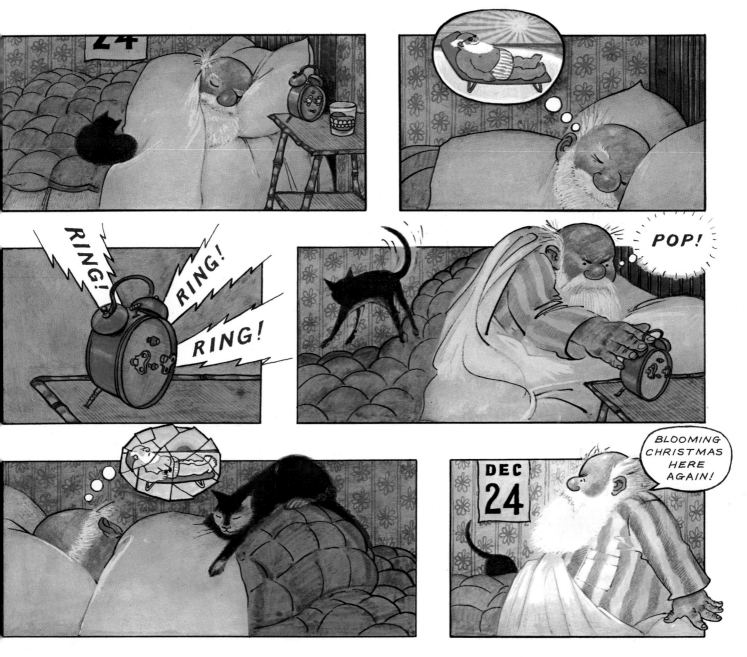

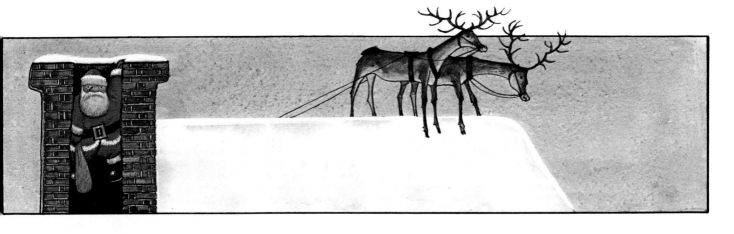

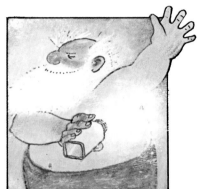

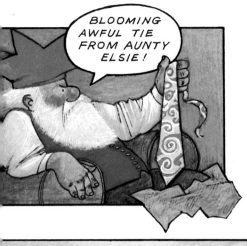

The End

Father Christmas goes on Holiday

For Jean

Father Christmas goes on Holiday

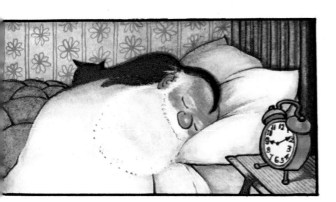

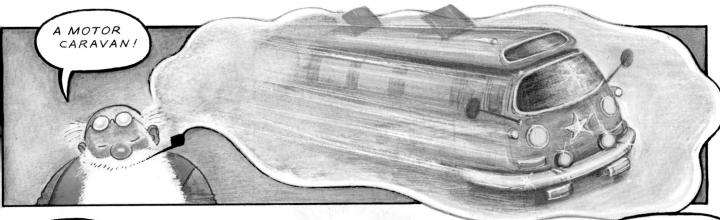

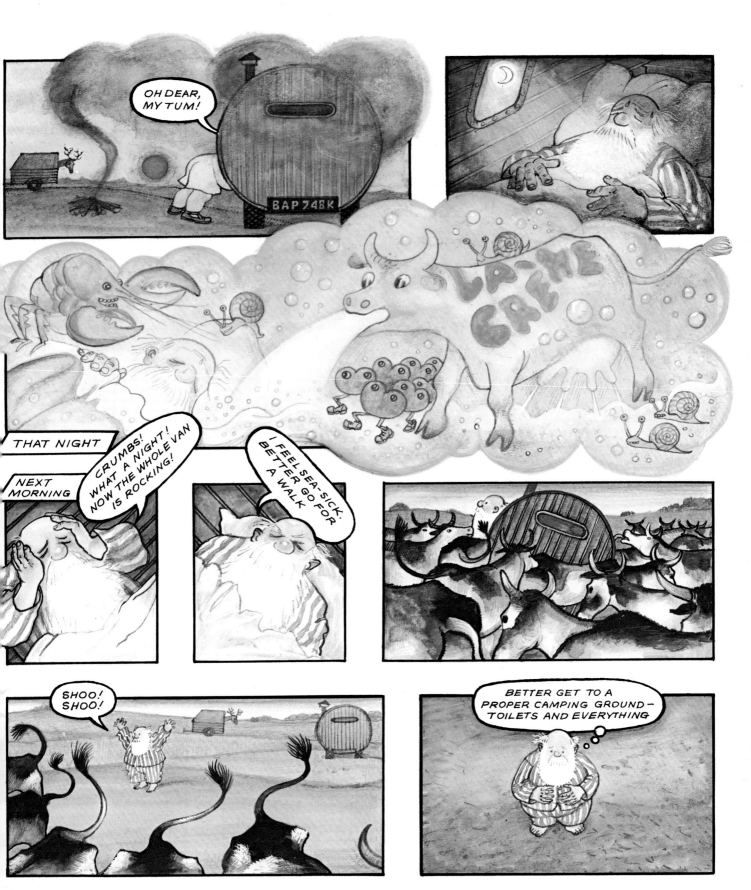

The End